The Lady in Blue

The Jumanos Meet Sor Maria de Ágreda

By Cynthia Jordan

Edited by Kathryn Louie

This book is dedicated with love and appreciation
to my mother *Margarita Estela Solis Jordan*

Special thanks to *Bishop Michael Pfeifer* for preserving *Sor Maria's* story, *Elizabeth Flores* for her matriarchal wisdom and devotion, *Tilly Chandler* for her support, and historian, *Enrique Madrid* for his insight and efforts in proudly honoring his ancestors, the *Jumanos*.

We also want to thank *Victor Mancilla* and *Christian Hernandez* with *Eravision Films* for their artistic contributions and generosity in allowing us to take photos for this project during their filming of the documentary, ***"The Needle and The Thread,"*** the story of *Sor Maria de Ágreda* and the *Jumanos*.

This book is a labor of love written
by Cynthia Jordan
with speculation and imagination from stories acquired
from Marilyn Fedewa's book *Mystical Lady in Blue*,
and Jumano historian, Enrique Madrid.
(Audio book available)

On April 2, 1602 in the city of Ágreda, Spain, Francisco Coronel and his wife Catalina de Arana were blessed with the birth of a baby girl they named Maria. Her mother could see that her daughter, even at a young age, was filled with the understanding of God's love. Every day little Maria asked her mother to read to her from the Bible.

When she was only four-years old, Maria received the sacrament of Confirmation from Bishop Diego de Yepes. "Little Maria's heart overflows with love and divine understanding from the Holy Spirit," he told her parents. This made Maria's parents happy and proud of their young daughter.

Maria was completely devoted to Jesus and his blessed mother Mary. She spent hours in prayer every day and was known by all as Maria de Jesus. When she was twelve, Maria decided to enter a monastery. As her parents prepared to accompany her there, her mother, Catalina had a vision that she would convert the family home into a convent where she and her daughters would serve as nuns.

At first Maria's father did not like the idea at all. Eventually he agreed to his wife's request and he himself entered the Franciscan order as a lay brother. The Coronel family home became the *Monastery of the Immaculate Conception*. The entire family had dedicated their lives to serving God.

Maria's life was very simple. She spent most of her time in her small room in prayer and meditation. Sometimes, days would pass before she left her room.

Prayer is when we speak to God. Meditation is when we listen and understand those things God desires for us to do. One day a strange thing happened. Maria's sister was walking by Maria's room when she saw that the door was slightly open. She looked inside and to her amazement Maria was floating in the air!

Quickly Maria's sister ran to tell the other sisters what she had seen. They all hurried to Maria's room and found that she was right. Maria was so deep in meditation that she had become weightless. Her spiritual body had elevated her physical body upward, defying the earthly laws of gravity. Maria was indeed floating in the air!

The sisters had never seen anything like it before. What was happening to their sister Maria de Jesus? Although they could see Maria's body, she was not aware of their presence at all. When she came out of her meditation, they were curious and asked her to please explain.

"But Maria… you were floating in the air like a humming-bird over a flower. What was that? Should we be frightened?"

Maria shook her head and smiled. "No, dear sisters. At first I believed it was a dream. Now I know that God has a special mission for me.

"What I am about to tell you must stay within the walls of this convent. When I was a child, I saw a play in the village square that greatly impressed me. The play told a story about indigenous people in the New World. I decided right then and there that I wanted to tell them about the great love that Jesus Christ has for them and the wonderful stories of his life."

"But Sor Maria… that is impossible. We have made a vow to never leave the convent. There is a massive ocean between Ágreda in Spain and the New World."

Maria's eyes were shining bright like stars twinkling on a moonless night. "Dear sisters. Do you believe that all things are possible with God?"

"Yes, of course, but…"

"Good. Then you will believe me when I tell you that God has taken me to heaven where I was told that I will become friends with the Jumanos. They are nomadic traders and hunters in the New World. Because of this they have relatives throughout the land. The Jumanos speak and understand many different dialects and are master communicators.

Right now the Jumanos know nothing about Jesus, Mother Mary, or the Trinity. I am going to change that. As I share God's divine message, the Jumanos will spread the word throughout the different tribes. The Jumanos are a peace-loving people with a strong sense of family as well as spirituality."

"But sister…"

"Now if you will please excuse me, I need to be alone," Maria smiled.

Meanwhile, far away in the unexplored western plains of the New World, there stood a rocky cliff that was sacred to the Jumano people. At the top of the bluff was a spiritual portal they saw as a magical pathway to heaven. The land surrounding the cliff held a special spiritual energy that cannot be explained, only felt in a heart that was true.

This is where the Jumano people came to celebrate their spirituality and understanding of harmony throughout the universe.

At the same time Maria de Jesus was sharing her mission with the sisters at the monastery, little Tula was getting an education from her mother about the paintings on the bluff.

"You see the paintings made with the red rock, little Tula? They were made by our ancestors. Each painting has meaning and they tell the story of the Jumano people. Can you see the buffalo? The sun? The arrow?"

"You see that painting that looks like a man walking up to heaven? That means the man's life is over and he is going to join the Great Spirit in the sky. See the bird? That means his soul is taking flight. The other symbols show that he lived a full life."

"I see a hammer!"

"Very good, Tula. When the sun is just right on the longest day a shadow makes a path and it looks as if the man is walking up to heaven.

"Now let's walk down a little way where I can show you a very important painting. It is directly in front of the great stone where the shaman stands. When the days become cold there is one night that is the longest of all nights. The day after that night occurs, we celebrate the days becoming long again. This is most important because the sun gives us light, warmth and healthy crops for food to eat. The paintings are gifts from our ancestors and teach us much wisdom."

After Tula's mother explained the rocks, her grandmother had another lesson to share.

"Hold up your hand, Tula. How many fingers do you have?"

"Five."

"Yes, there are five. It takes five members to make a family… five families to make a band… five bands to make a clan… five clans to make a pueblo… five pueblos to make a tribe… five tribes to make a nation and five nations to make a confederation. Women and children must be protected for all to survive. That is why you will always be important, little Tula."

Maria went into her small room and shut the door. She had instructed the sisters not to interfere with her sacred time with God. No peepholes, no conversation by her door; Maria wanted complete privacy. As far as she was concerned she had a mission to fulfill and she was fully committed.

Fifteen-year-old Maria de Jesus sat on her bed and gently placed her hands on her lap. She loved the time when she was in spiritual oneness with her Creator. It was twilight and she could see the warm colors of the sunset quietly transforming the sky, bringing an end to another day of precious living. Slowly Maria closed her eyes. "Thank you, dear God, for all of your blessings. I am your servant. *Thy will be done*."

For a short time Maria was aware that her breath was deep. Then suddenly, her entire being was alive with intense exhilaration and she felt as if she was flying. Brilliant colors were everywhere and the great love that surrounded her like a warm blanket made her feel safe and secure.

Then in an instant Maria began to see things she had never seen before. She saw oak trees strategically positioned upon a vast, grassy plain, wild buffalo herds and then a long, green river with some kind of prickly plant growing along its banks. There was a part of her that thought she was in a glorious dream, but her spirit was aware that she was dancing in the wonder of a miracle, that magical place where we are one with all that is. Maria was dancing in the loving light of God.

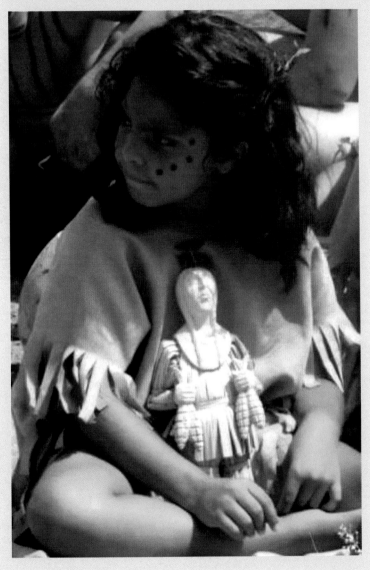

Little Tula was playing with her doll when she suddenly felt a warmth rush over her heart. Jesus once said that when we look at the world through the eyes of a child we can see the kingdom of heaven. Tula could feel the *love* that was coming to her. She could feel the *love* of Maria and the *love* of God. She looked towards the bluff where earlier that day she had learned about the paintings from her mother. Tula, the little Jumano child pure in spirit, was the first to see the beautiful lady in blue.

A warm breeze blew across her face as Maria gazed upon the land and the Jumano people who were there. When she saw little Tula looking at her, she smiled and gave her a friendly wave.

Tula waved back. She could see a shimmering light surrounding the lady wearing the blue cape. Tula saw her cousin Lala walking towards the lady. She held on to her doll and watched.

Lala was one of the lovely young maidens of the Jumano tribe. Everyone knew that she was kind and pure of heart. Birds and bunnies would play with her and butterflies would land and flutter in her hand. Tula watched as she saw Lala approach the beautiful lady in blue.

"Hello, my name is Lala. Are you the one in my dream?"

"Hello, dear one. I am Maria, your new friend."

Grandmother was concerned. She could see her granddaughter speaking but there was no one there. Grandmother was wise and the matriarch of the clan. Everyone listened when grandmother spoke. Instinctively she could feel something wonderful was about to happen.

Quietly and cautiously, grandmother approached the tree, then stopped in her tracks. She could see Maria! Grandmother was looking at a beautiful maiden in blue. She saw that she was not much older than Lala and could feel in her heart that the young woman was pure in spirit.

"Venga (come). Isa-ke' (tree)" Maria motioned with a friendly wave.

"Hello, I am Maria. I am here to share a story about a man you will come to love. His name is Jesus. *Tapetao*," Maria smiled. "*Piye-e*."

Grandmother and Lala also smiled. *Tapetao* means *to love* and *piye-e* is *friend*. Although the women were from two very different parts of the world, somehow by a miracle from the Holy Spirit they were able to speak and understand each other.

"Abuelita," Maria graced pointing at Grandmother and looking at Lala, she complimented, "Senorita bonita". Maria put both hands over her heart. "Jesus tiene un corazon con mucho amor… *pen-'e (heart) tapetao."* Maria looked and saw the clan was walking towards her. Leading the way was little Tula.

Maria told the Jumanos about Jesus and the great love he had for them. She told them how he walked on water, cured the sick and healed the blind. Picking up two sticks from the ground and binding them with long blades of grass, Maria made a cross and, with tears rolling down her face, she shared the story of his passion and then taught the Jumanos how to make the sign of the cross.

"In the name of the Father, and of the Son, and the Holy Spirit, Amen," she said touching her forehead, her heart, her left then right shoulder, and then kissing her hand. Tula did it with her and then all the Jumanos followed.

Maria was especially fascinated with the buffalo.

"Tell me about them, Abuelita. Tell me the story of yotson-le."

"Our ancestors were half man and half buffalo. They are our totem."

"Totem?"

"The buffalo are family… our brothers and sisters. We see them as sacred because we need them to survive. The buffalo give us food, robes for warmth and we use their bones for tools. No part is ever wasted. We honor and give thanks and appreciation for their great sacrifice so that we may live. The most sacred is the white buffalo. Only those with a heart that is brave and true can find it. I have seen the white buffalo in my lifetime."

"Like the buffalo, Jesus gave his life so that we may live, Abuelita."

Three days and two nights had passed when Maria said goodbye to the Jumano people. Tula wanted her to stay.

"It is only for a few days, little Tula. I must go back to my convent in Spain. When I return I will teach you a game. I promise."

That evening at dusk, Maria found a peaceful spot by the river. Her heart was full and she gave thanks to God for giving her the gift of bilocation. Again she began to breathe deeply and in a moment she felt as if she were flying, surrounded by a brilliant, loving light that felt safe and warm. Her journey seemed timeless. Slowly, as she opened her eyes, Maria found herself sitting upright on her bed in her small room in the convent. For a moment there was only silence and then, Maria could hear the gradual melodic song of birds greeting the sun like small minstrels as the dawn was breaking, welcoming a new day.

Maria went to the garden. She felt rested and at the same time invigorated with joy as she thought about her new Jumano friends. One by one the sisters joined her. Maria was glowing with *Love* from the Holy Spirit.

"Sor Maria! What has happened??"

"Oh sisters! I have been on the most glorious adventure! God has given me a mission to teach Native Americans in the New World. It is by the power of the Holy Spirit that my spirit is able to cross the ocean and be here and there at the same time. I saw buffalo and a river that has big mussels with beautiful pink pearls! I met the Jumanos. Their skin is brown and they have black markings on their bodies. They pull their hair up in a knot on top of their head and decorate it with a feather! The chief has a scar on his face."

The sisters listened with fascination as Maria revealed her adventures about her miraculous journey. There would be hundreds more to come.

The next week, Maria returned. This time the Jumanos welcomed her with great love and open arms. Maria kept her promise to Tula and taught her games to play with the other children. Maria found herself to be both the teacher and the student. She marveled at her new friends and especially loved the wisdom and insight of Abuelita

One day the grandmother said something Maria had never forgotten. "Life itself is spiritual. We are one with all that is."

Tula held a special place in Maria's heart. Grandmother had told Maria that she was named Tula because she had been born at the time of year when the leaves turn brilliant colors before they fall to the ground.

"I have a present for you, Tula. They are prayer beads we call a rosary. As you can see there are five strands of ten beads. We say the *Hail Mary* on each bead and the *Our Father* and *Glory Be* in between. The rosary is a prayer request to Mother Mary, the Blessed Mother of Jesus. It will bring your soul peace all of your life."

Grandmother told Maria that the Jumanos looked for the beauty that surrounded them and saw all of life as sacred.

"The women and children are most important. Without them the tribe cannot survive. We are the power that sustains life."

Grandmother taught Maria the call to the seven directions. "The Jumanos believe that life is a miracle and all that surrounds us is sacred. We look to the east where the day begins, then to the west where at the end of the day the sun fades away and the stars appear in the night. We look to the north from where the wind whistles and moans and to the south where the buffalo graze. We look above us to the sun, the moon and the stars. We look below us and give thanks to our Earth Mother whose gifts are bountiful. Finally we look into our heart, the place where the soul is alive and *Love* abounds."

Maria told the Jumanos that it was important to practice the sacraments to receive God's grace. "We must bring missionaries here so you can be baptized with ebad (water) just as Jesus was baptized in the river Jordan."

Because the river was sacred to the Jumano people, Maria's words rang true. A group of men decided to go west and bring priests back to their people. Because of their many travels they knew they could find the priests at the Isleta pueblo near the river the Spanish called Rio del Norte, today known as the Rio Grande.

The band of Jumanos had made several attempts to bring missionaries to their people but to no avail. Then a series of events happened perfectly that changed everything.

Maria had told her priest about her spiritual travels to the Jumano people. He wrote a letter to the archbishop in Mexico City who in turn wrote to Father Benavides at the Isleta mission. Benavides oversaw Catholic conversions in the New World. The letters told of a nun in Ágreda, Spain who claimed she had taken several hundred mystical journeys to the New World to teach Native Americans the love of Jesus. A few days after receiving the letter the Jumanos arrived again.

"We were sent by the *Lady in Blue*. Our people want to be baptized."

Father Benavides was intrigued and even a little perplexed. He had just received the archbishop's letter only days before. Benavides was very careful with where he would send missionaries and supplies.

"I will send two of my padres with you," Benavides agreed. "This is most unusual but somehow I feel it is the right thing to do."

The journey was long. The Jumanos took the padres through land that was known only to the indigenous people of the New World. The padres were amazed at their skills and understanding of the vast, barren land. There was always food to eat and water to drink.

The padres developed a genuine respect for their new Jumano friends. Although their story was hard to believe, they were enchanted with the Jumanos' strong will and determination. In their hearts they knew that they were being led by the Holy Spirit and doing God's will.

"Lala…Tula… the time is near. The missionaries will be here soon. We must tell everyone to be ready to greet them and prepare themselves for baptism. There is so much to be thankful for. We are truly blessed and there is much to celebrate."

"Come with me," Lala said, taking Tula's hand. "Let us tell Abuelita."

"Look, Padre! Look!! There are thousands of them! No missionaries have ever set foot on this land! This is a fantastic miracle and we are truly blessed to be a part of it. Madre de Dios!"

Abuelita and Lala presented the padres with a cross covered with flowers. Their hearts were bursting with appreciation for their long journey.

Deeply touched by the gesture, the missionaries could feel warm, salty tears fill their eyes as they accepted the gift.

Although Sor Maria was there, the padres could not see her. Only her Jumano friends were able to celebrate her quiet presence. So many times God works in mysterious ways. Just because others cannot see a spiritual being, it does not mean they are not there. As far as Maria was concerned, her mission had just begun. There were still thousands more indigenous people in the New World who needed to hear the story of Jesus.

Walking towards the river, one of the padres spotted an exquisite looking pink shell with a lustrous pink pearl lying on the ground.

"Look at this!" he exclaimed, holding the pearl up towards the sun. See how it glistens and shines. How beautiful it is! I will use the shell to baptize the people today."

The people joyfully gathered at the river. They had waited a long time for this day. It was their day of rebirth, a cleansing of the soul. Today they would become one with the family of God, the family of *Love*.

They began chanting in song to celebrate this great event.

"*Jesus… Namoe-e… Tapetao,*" (Jesus… Light… Love)

From the other side of the river, the Lady in Blue watched as the Jumanos and their brothers and sisters from miles around receive the blessed sacrament of baptism. Joy and laughter filled the air as the warm western wind gently blew on their happy faces. Maria's heart was full.

Lala watched as the padre baptized her younger brother. "I baptize you in the name of the Father, and of the Son and of the Holy Spirit. Go in peace."

"What is baptism," Lala asked her grandmother.

"Baptism is a ceremony much like when we burn the white sage to clean away bad energy, Lala. It cleanses the soul so that we can join the family of Jesus."

Sor Maria made over 500 visits to many Native American tribes in the New World. Finally the day came when Maria would say good-bye.

"I will miss my friend, Mama," Tula sighed.

"The Lady in Blue will forever be in our hearts and the hearts of future generations to come, Tula. We will make sure of it."

There is a legend that is told in Texas about the bluebonnet flower that blossoms throughout the land in the spring.

It is said that when the Jumanos awoke the morning after Maria's last visit, bluebonnet flowers grew in abundance everywhere her blue cape had touched the ground. A memorable gift from the *Lady in Blue*.

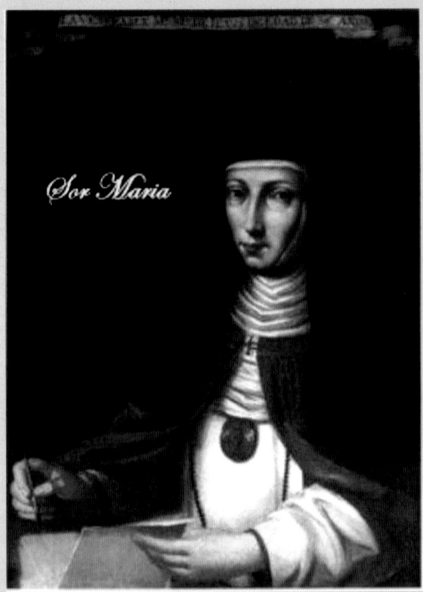

Maria Jesus de Ágreda was inspired by the Blessed Mother to write her story so that we could better understand Mary, the mother of Jesus. Sor Maria's work is known as *The Mystical City of God* and has been celebrated throughout the world as a spiritual masterpiece.

Today Sor Maria's incorrupted body lies peacefully in a glass coffin in Ágreda, Spain. Those of us who love her will always know her as our beloved Lady in Blue.

The Bluebonnet Song
by Cynthia Jordan

In the great land of Texas
In the dawn of the spring
There's a beautiful flower
That blankets the plains
It's shaped like a bonnet
So lovely a hue
A beautiful gift
From the Lady in Blue

(chorus)
Walk with God the bluebonnet sings
There is peace and light in His Love
Love one another with a love that's true
This is the message from the Lady in Blue

She came to the Native in the spirit of peace
A mystical journey a spiritual dream
The people could see her in a vision of blue
And they became friends with the lady in Blue *(chorus)*

So if you're in Texas and you happen to see
Bluebonnets dancing wild and free
Think of your blessings with joy and gratitude
As the wind sings the song of the Lady in Blue *(chorus)*

Made in the
USA
Columbia, SC